MW00604164

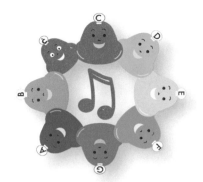

Preschool Prodigies

CHAPTER SIX

6

By: Robert and Samantha Young

Illustrations: Robert Young with art licensed at FreePik.com

Published by: Young Music, LLC

ISBN:978-0999210147
Copyright © 2017
Preschool Prodigies and Young Music, LLC
2358 Dutch Neck Road
Smyrna, DE 19977

Prodigies Playground
THIS BOOK BELONGS TO:

_____

Dear families & teachers,

Welcome back to Preschool Prodigies! In Chapter 6, we'll focus more on the notes Fa, Sol and La, and play lots of Holiday themed songs!

Depending on when you start the program, you might even want to do some of this chapter around the holidays. If that means you have to go a little out of order for now, that's okay! In the future, we may separate the holiday songs into their own supplemental section, but for now, they're integrated into this chapter.

If you find that you need some extra material as a result of the seasonal content being not-in-season, definitely visit PsP Melodies. The Melodies series focuses solely on the Solfège hand-signs, and it's an easy detour whenever you need a little bit of extra material.

There is also an Extra Practice Chapter at the end of the Preschool Prodigies videos, that focuses on different pairs of bells. These are a good supplement as well. Plus, we have a growing library of performance tracks that feature scrolling music with zero instruction. You can use these to perfect songs, put on recitals (mock or real) and really zoom in on mastering specific songs.

If you've made it this far, I'm confident you'll have no problem mixing and matching the different materials to fit your needs. If you have any questions, don't hesitate to e-mail us at Support@PreschoolProdigies.com.

Happy Musicing,

– Mr. Rob & the Prodigies Team

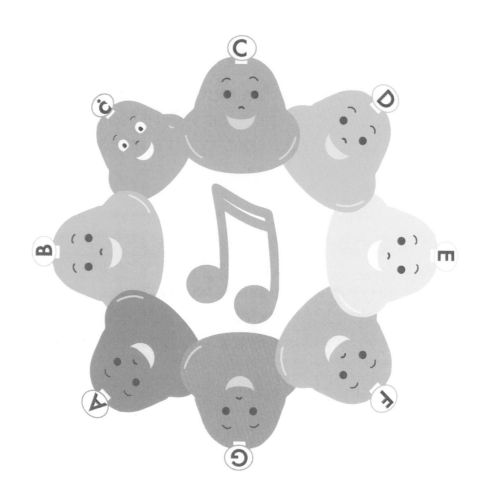

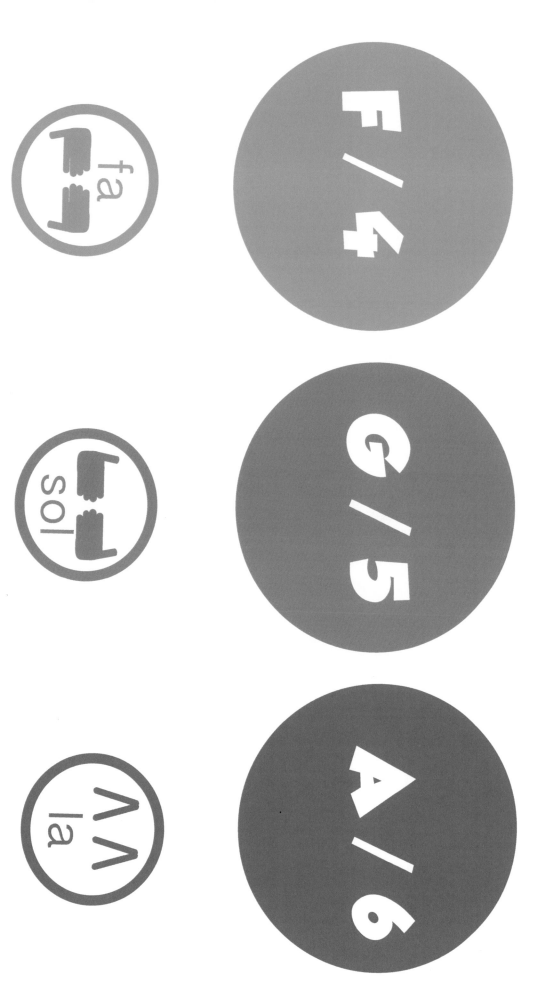

Fa, Sol, La Bell Mat

Use this bell mat for lesson 6.1

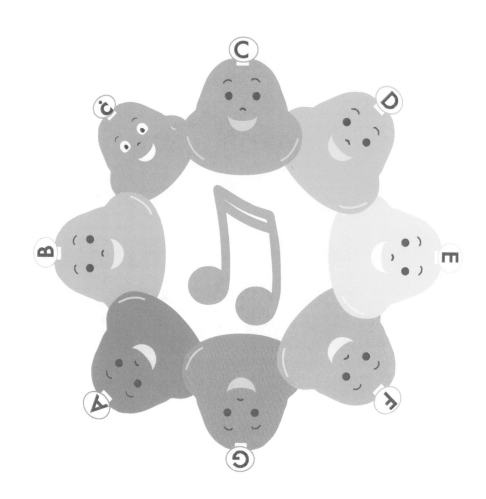

Chapter 6 ❀ Section 1: Fa Sol La Intro ♫ Lesson Guide

Objective

By the end of this section, students should be able to differentiate between the notes F, G and A.

Overview

In this section, students review Fa, Sol and La, then play a variety of holiday themed songs.

Essential Question

How can a student differentiate the notes F, G and A?

Instruction Tips

Hang the poster from this section in your music practice space and reference it often. Try conducting your learner just using this poster.

Materials

- F Bell • G Bell • A Bell
- Green Crayon • Teal Crayon
- Purple Crayon
- Fa Sol La Intro Video Access
- Workbook pages: 8-17
- Scissors

Table of Contents

Fa Sol La Song Sheets	8
F Letter Trace	10
A Letter Trace	11
Fa, Sol, La Hand-Signs	12
Hand-Sign Cut-Outs	15
Circle the Fs	17

Complementary Activities

Have one student use the hand-sign poster to conduct the class in a "point and response" hand-signing exercise.

Section 6.1 Video Annotations

0:00 Explain to students that this is a warm up with the notes Fa, Sol and La. They should take out their F, G and A bells.

1:49 Pause here and ask your learner what Mr. Rob means when he says, "skip up".

2:14 Pause here and review the three hand-signs for these three notes before Mr. Rob introduces them.

Fa Sol La Warm Up
Lesson 6.1
☆☆☆☆☆

Fa   Sol   La   Fa   Sol   La

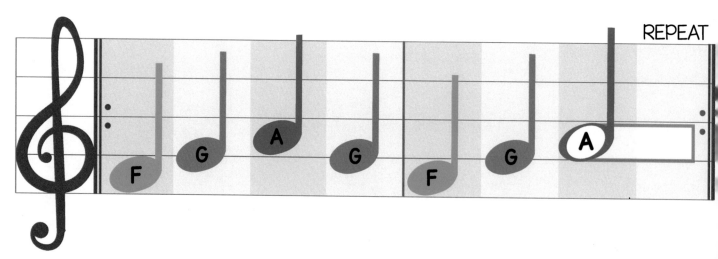

Fa   Sol   La   Sol   Fa   Sol   La

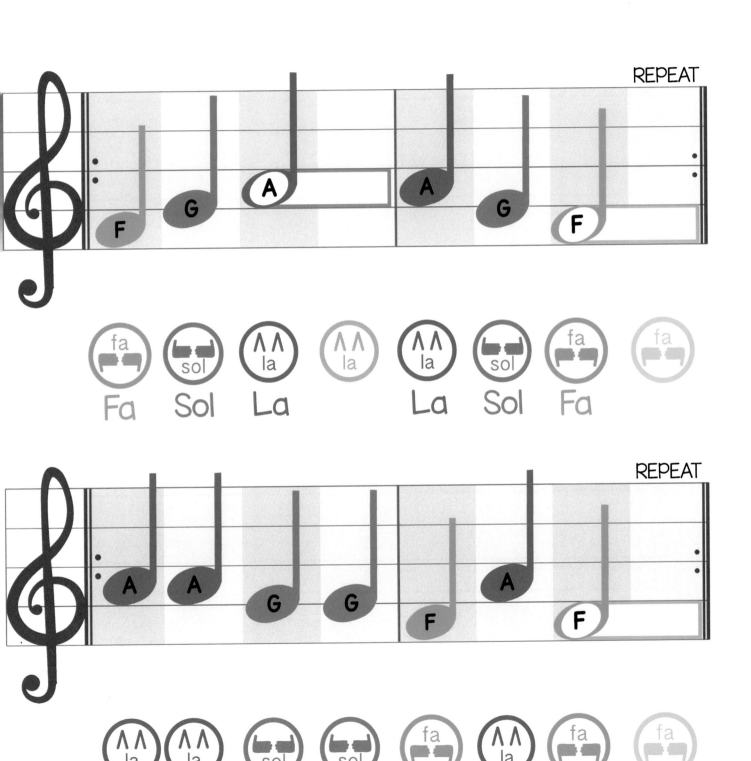

f f f f f f f f f f f

4 4 4 4 4 4 four four

green green green

fa fa fa fa fa fa fa

F F F F F F F F F

4 4 4 4 4 4 FOUR FOUR

GREEN GREEN GREEN

FA FA FA FA FA FA FA

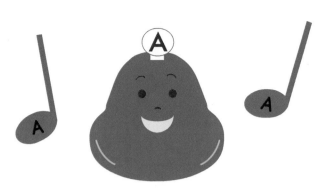

a a a a a a a a a a a

6 6 6 6 6 6 six six six

purple purple purple

la la la la la la la la la

A A A A A A A A A A A

6 6 6 6 6 6 SIX SIX

PURPLE PURPLE

LA LA LA LA LA LA LA LA

Fa Sol La Hand-Signs

In this chapter, we'll learn and practice the hand-signs for the next three musical notes: Fa, Sol and La. The signs will make it easier for you and your learner to feel the different sensations of each note.

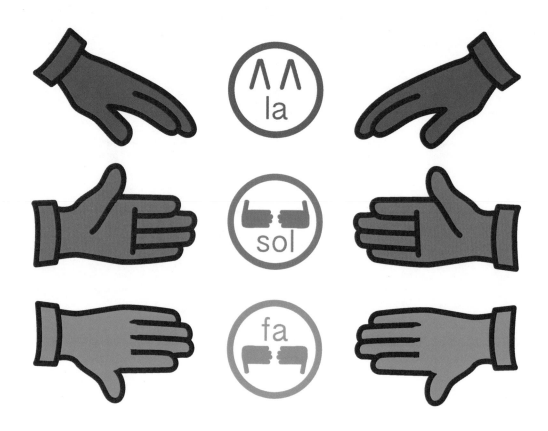

The detailed drawings of the hand-signs are visible here.

In the middle are some of the simplified versions that we use inside the Playground videos.

The simplified signs are easier to write on a board if you're a teacher and easy enough for kids to draw.

For extra practice, try playing a bell (Green, Teal or Purple) and then singing the Solfège note while making the hand-sign. Have your child sing and sign along, or even have them play a bell and then sing and sign.

Fa Sol La Hand-Signs
Point and Sign Poster

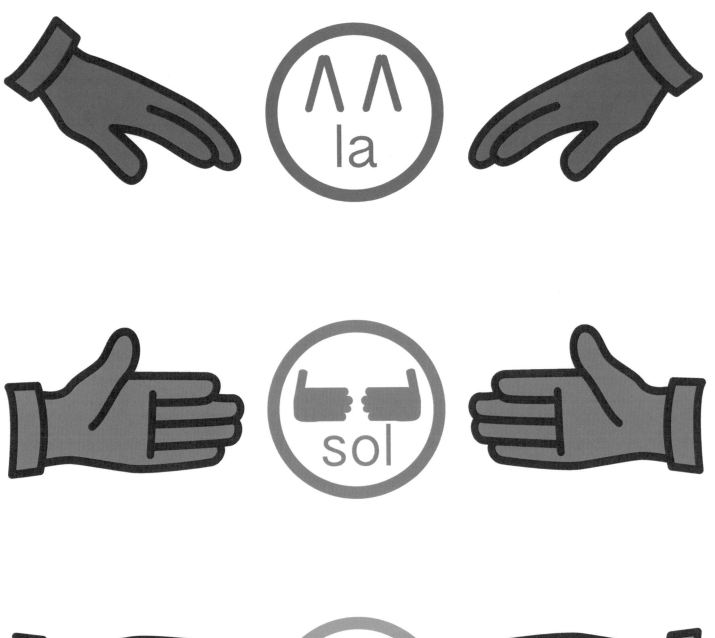

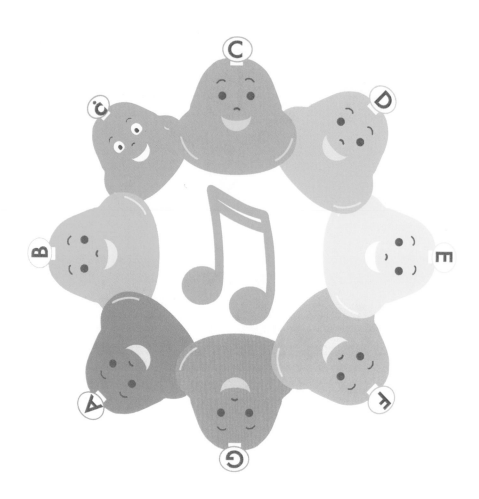

Hand-Sign Cut-Outs

Use these cut-outs to sequence your own Fa, Sol, La practice.

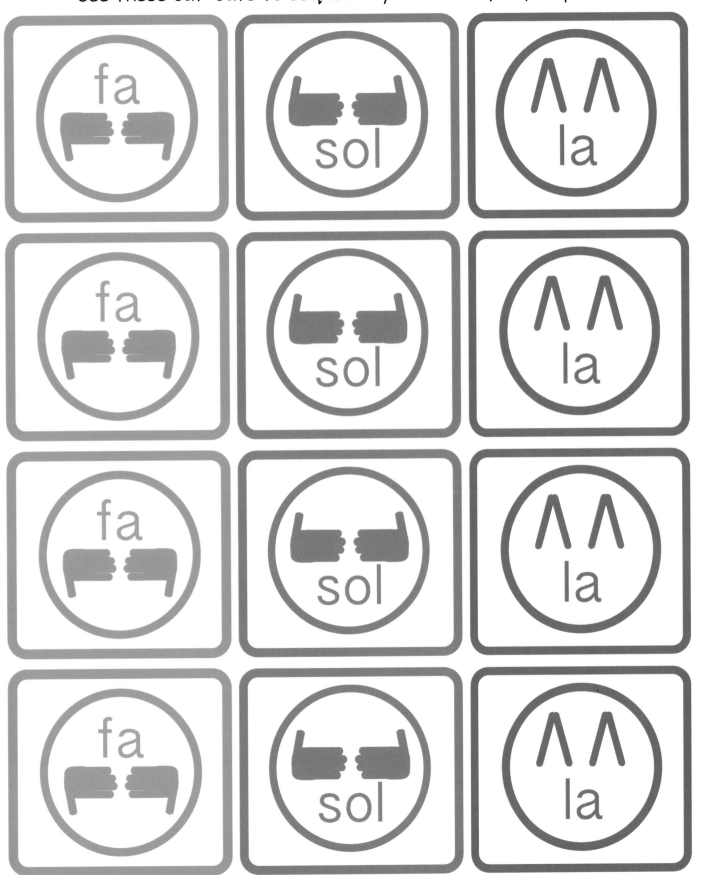

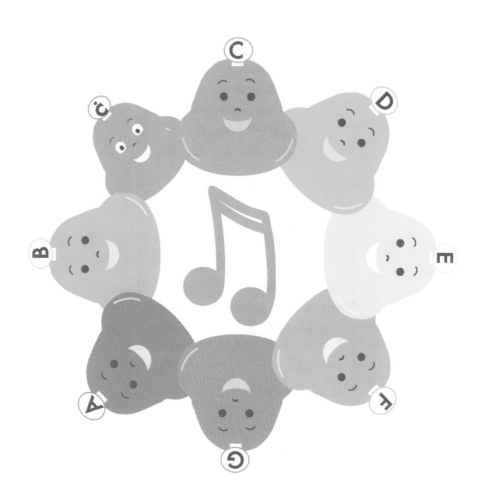

Circle the Fs

Trace the word below every picture, then
circle the picture in each row that begins with an F green.

frost

lights

wreath

cookie

reindeer

fir

elf

fireplace

gift

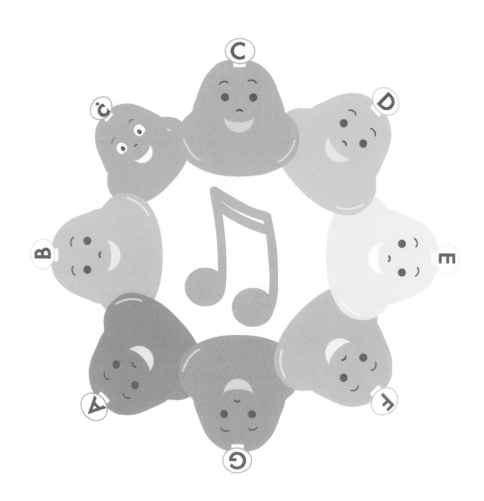

Chapter 6 ❄ Section 2: Jingle Bells ❄ Lesson Guide

Objective

By the end of this section, students should be able to play "Jingle Bells" and identify the Solfège name and color of F, G & A.

Overview

In this section, students play "Jingle Bells" and study the notes F, G & A.

Essential Question

How can a student identify F, G & A?

Instruction Tips

Students may want to play this song over and over again. Embrace their enthusiasm and comfort with the song and let them play it as much as time allows. Jingle Bells can be difficult for young learners, so the more practice, the better.

Materials

- C Bell • D Bell • E Bell • F Bell • G Bell
- Red Crayon • Orange Crayon • Yellow Crayon
- Green Crayon • Teal Crayon
- Jingle Bells Video Access
- Workbook pages: 20-27

Table of Contents

Jingle Bells Song Sheets	20
Write a Song Using Fa, Sol & La	24
Music Matching 1	25
Music Matching 2	26
Color the As	27

Complementary Activities

Ask your learner to create his or her own Fa, Sol, La pattern and play it for you, then play it back for him or her. Take turns creating a pattern for the other to replicate.

Section 6.2 Video Annotations

0:00 Explain to students that this video will use Do, Re, Mi, Fa & Sol. They should take out their C, D, E, F & G bells.

1:25 Mr. Rob shifts from playing the bells to hand-signing.

2:32 Students begin singing the lyrics to "Jingle Bells" while playing their bells.

3:56 Mr. Rob explains the difference between chorus and verse.

Jingle Bells
Chorus Melody Sheet
Lesson 6.2

☆☆☆☆☆

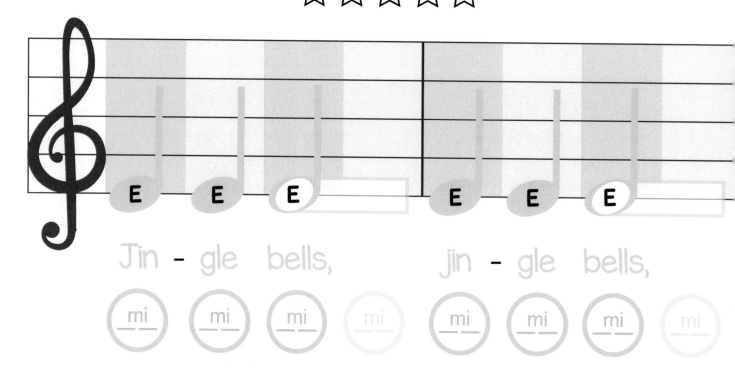

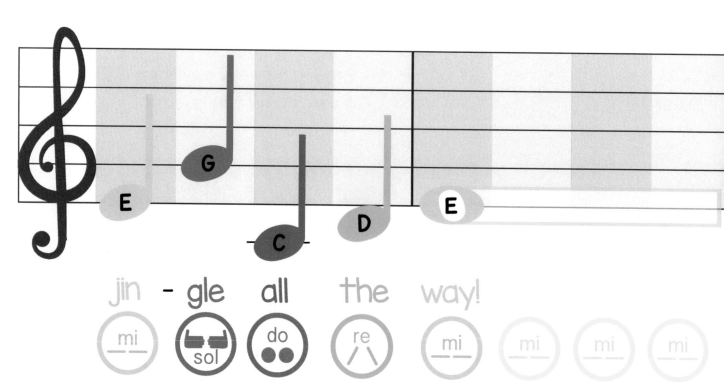

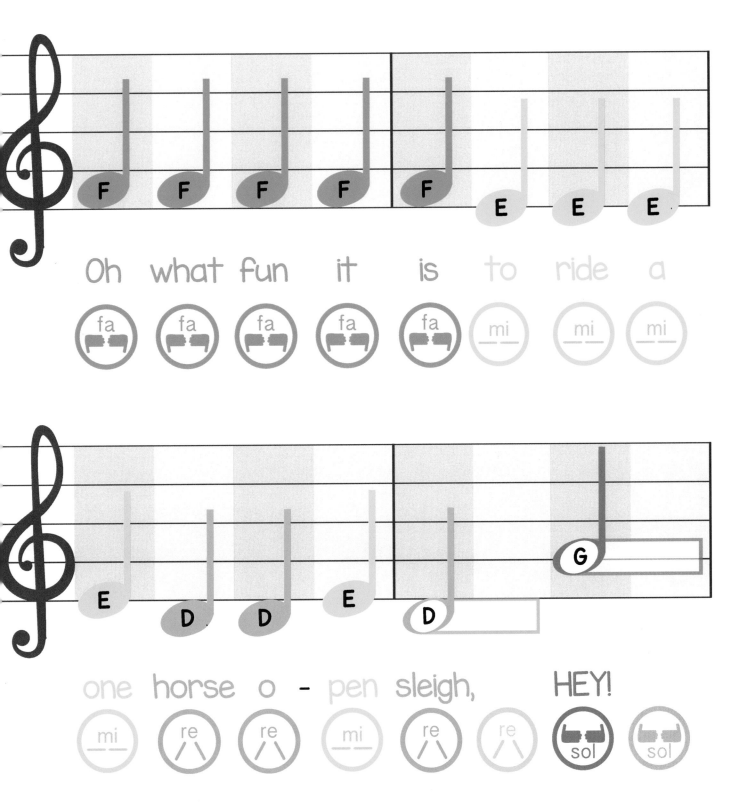

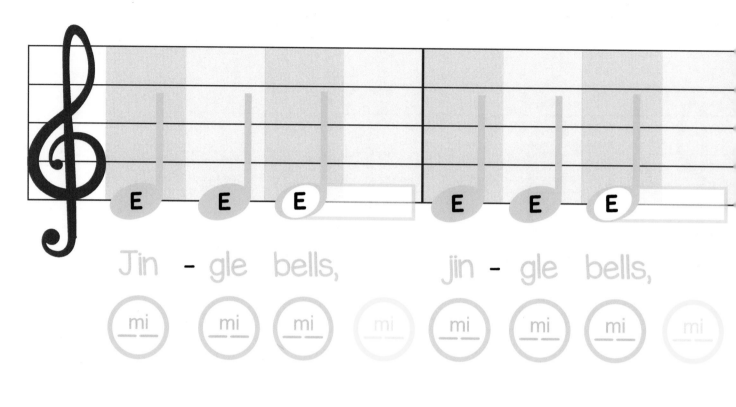

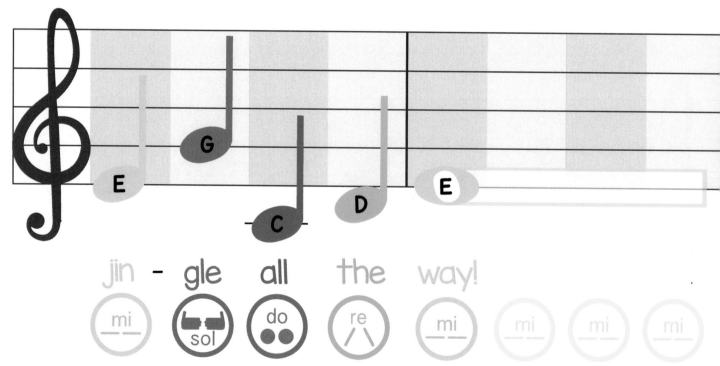

Write a Song Using

Title _____   Composer _____

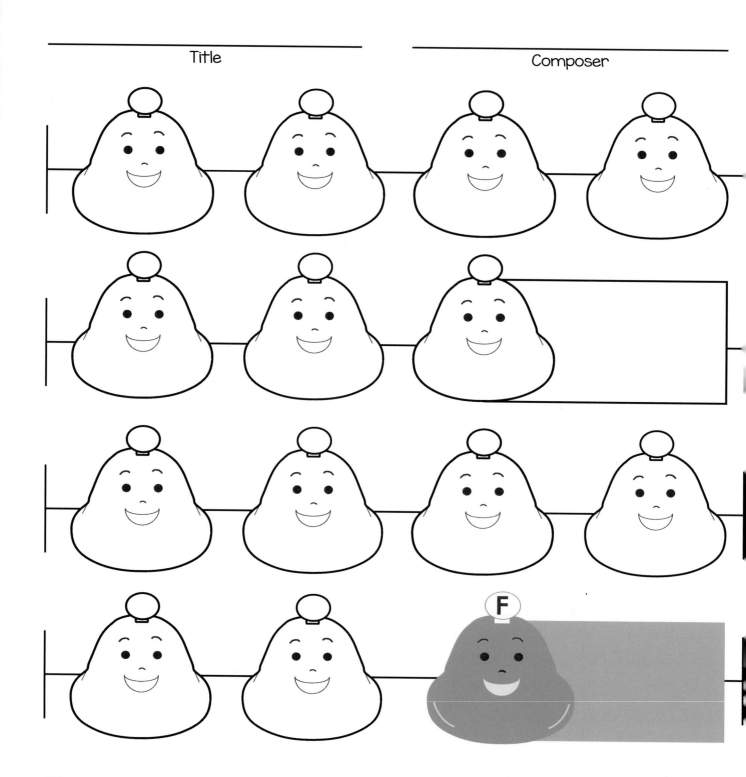

Music Matching I

We have lots of different ways to talk about our musical notes and sometimes they get mixed up!

Can you connect the bells to their Solfège words, scale degrees (numbers), and hand-signs?

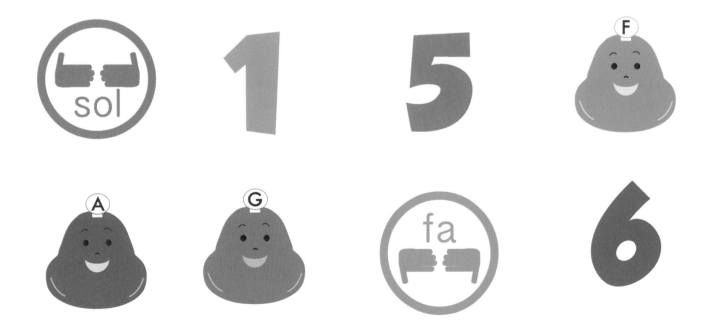

Music Matching 2

Circle the As

Trace the word below every picture, then
circle the picture in each row that begins with an A purple.

toy   candle   apple

star   airplane   pie

axe   skates   bow

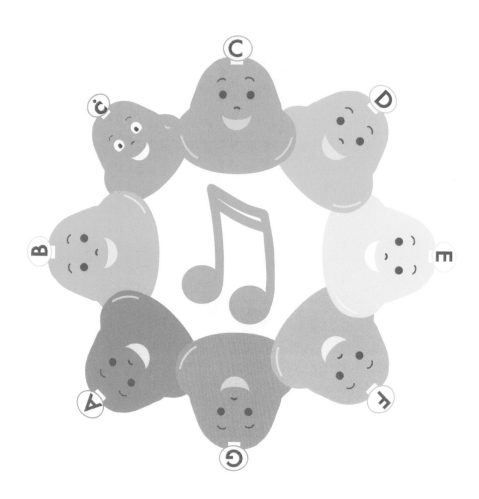

Chapter 6 ♪ Section 3: Ode to Joy ♪ Lesson Guide

Objective

By the end of this section, students should be able to play "Ode to Joy" and recall one thing about Beethoven.

Overview

In this section, students learn to play "Ode to Joy" and a few facts about the composer, Beethoven.

Essential Question

How can a student play Beethoven's "Ode to Joy"?

Instruction Tips

This song can be a little tricky for students. Give them plenty of opportunities to play it, including when they color the notes and draw the steps and skips between the scale degrees.

Materials

- C Bell • D Bell • E Bell • F Bell • G Bell
- Red Crayon • Orange Crayon
- Yellow Crayon • Green Crayon • Teal Crayon
- Ode to Joy Video Access
- Workbook pages: 30-38

Table of Contents

Ode to Joy Song Sheets   30

Match the Hand-Signs   34

Color the Notes   35

Ludwig Van Beethoven   37

Ode to Steps and Skips   38

Complementary Activities

Ask your learner if he or she can use any of the words learned in "Ludwig Van Beethoven" to make a new sentence.

Section 6.3 Video Annotations

0:00 Explain to students that in this video they will play another song with just the first five notes: C, D, E, F & G and that they should take out those bells.

1:45 Pause here and review the first five Solfège hand-signs. Practice with your learner before moving on in "Ode to Joy".

2:42 If students are struggling with the pace, go back to 1:45 and slow down the video a few clicks with the playback speed buttons.

4:52 Mr. Rob talks about transitioning to the piano for "Ode to Joy".

Ode to Joy
Lesson 6.3
☆☆☆☆☆

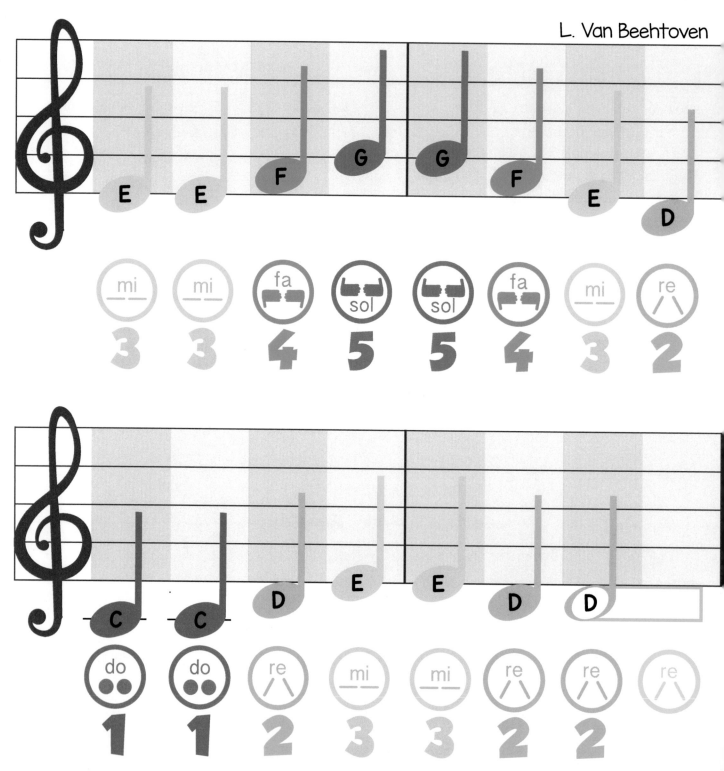

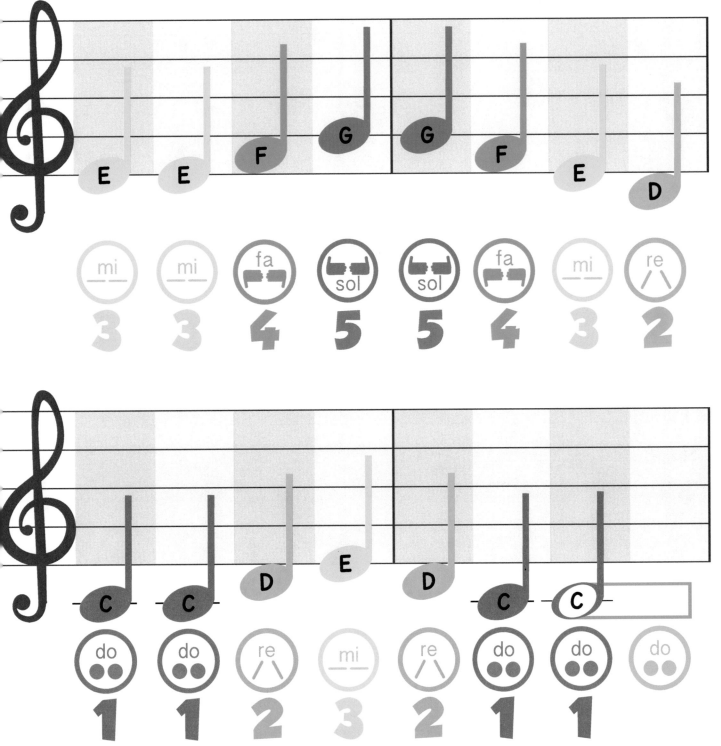

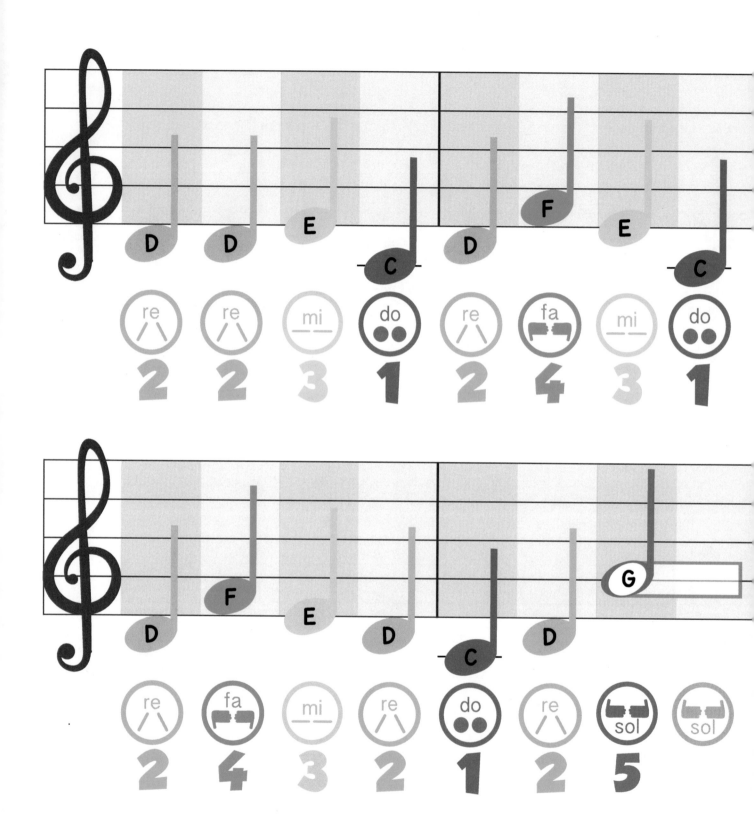

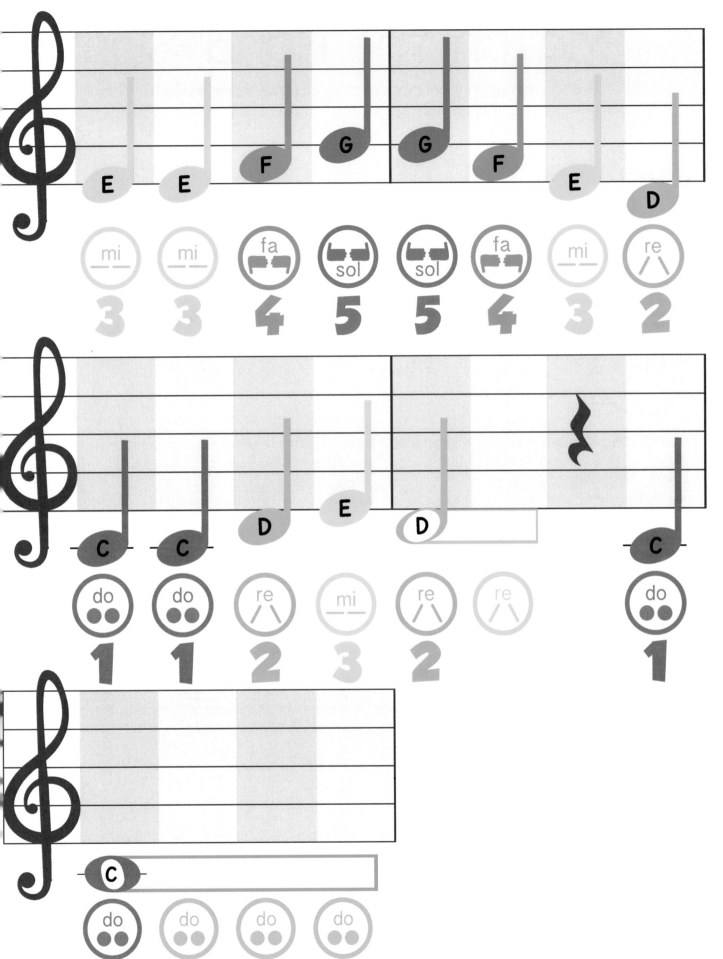

Match the Hand-Signs

Draw a line between the correct hand-sign and note it represents.

Color the Notes
Ode to Joy

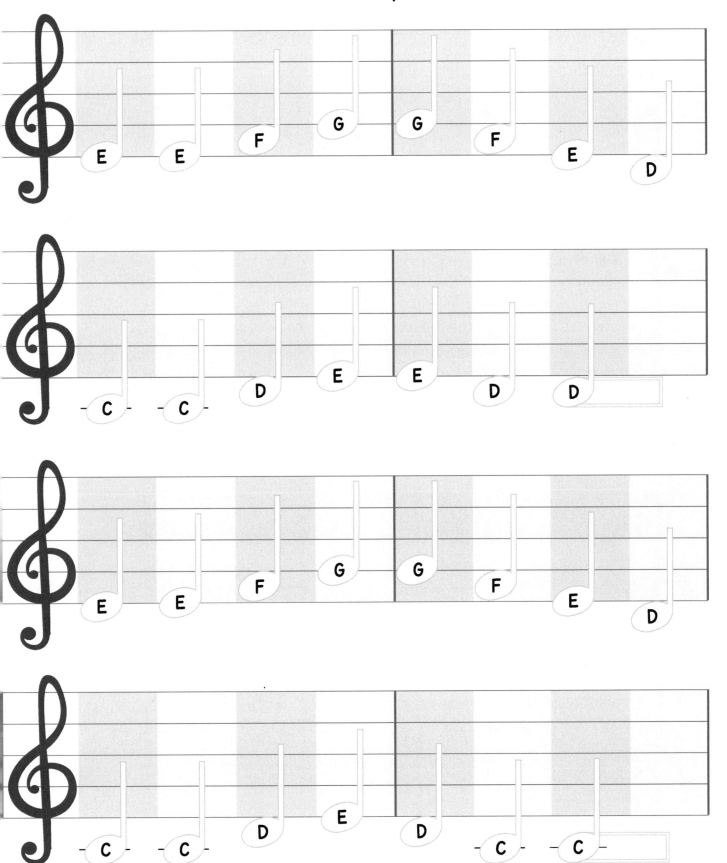

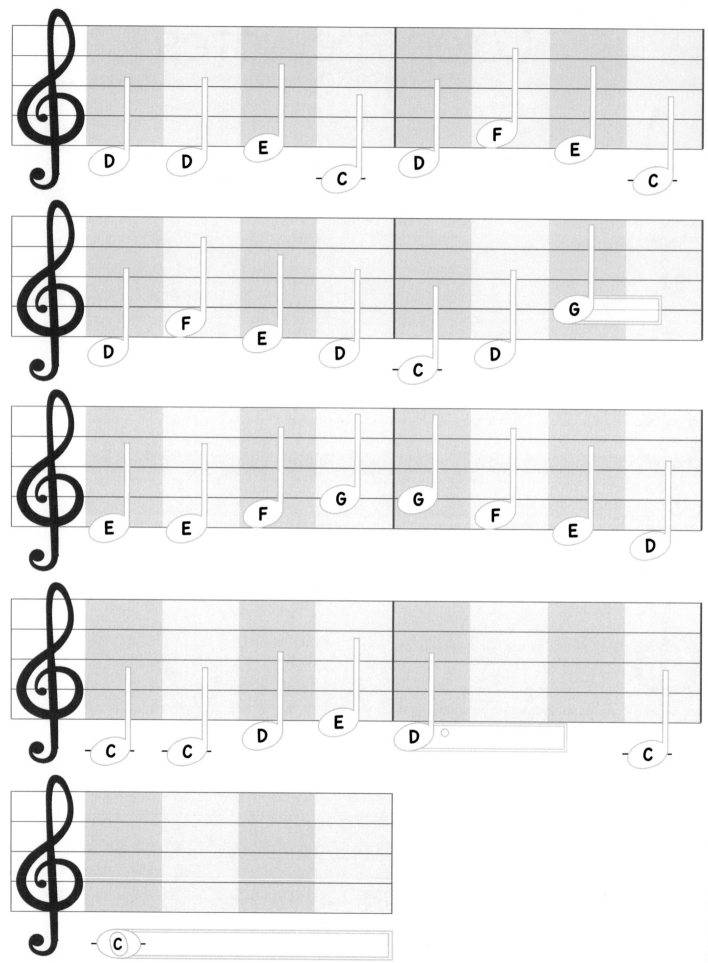

Ludwig Van Beethoven

The composer of this song is named Ludwig Van Beethoven. A composer is a person who writes music. Beethoven started playing music at a very early age, maybe even the same age as you! Beethoven played his first concert at age 7. He wrote the song "Ode to Joy" as part of his famous Ninth Symphony. Beethoven is considered a prodigy in our culture, or a young person with amazing abilities.

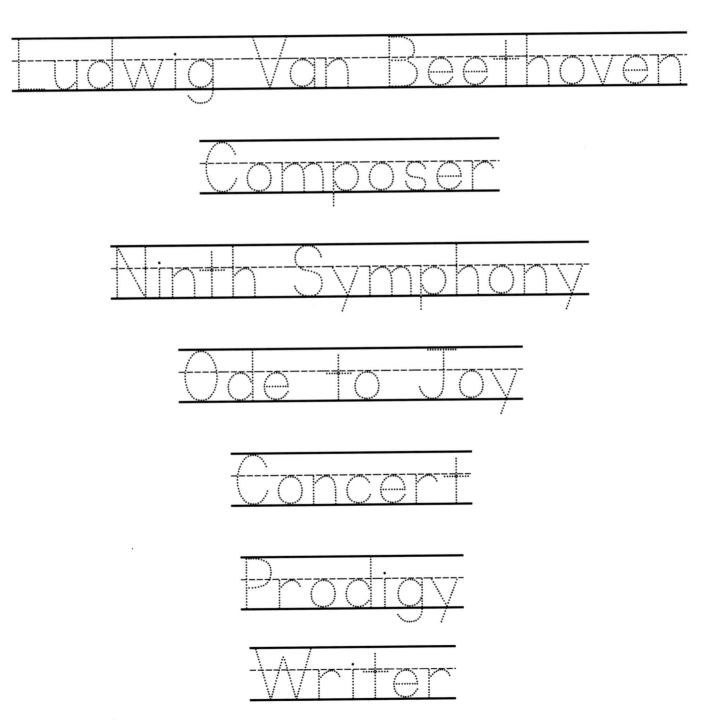

Ode to Steps & Skips

Ode to Joy uses many steps and a few skips. Can you draw the correct arrow to indicate steps or skips?

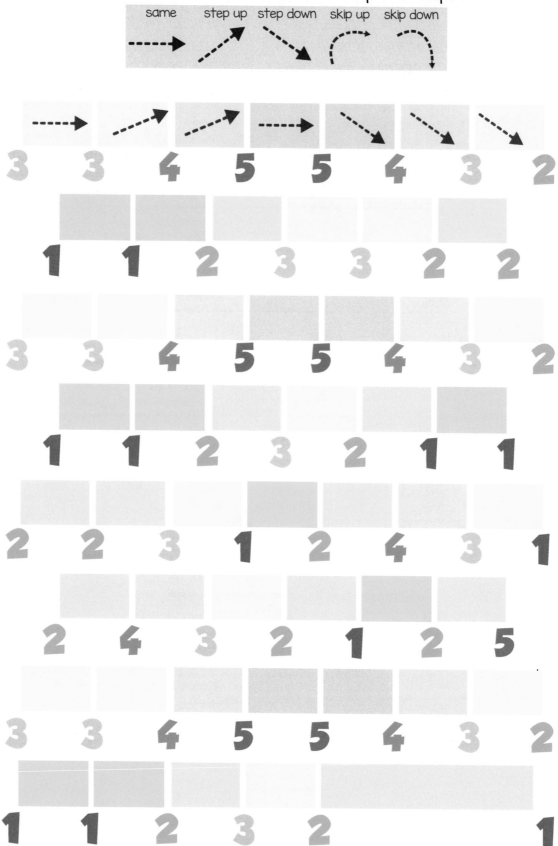

Chapter 6 ❄ Section R: Snow Day ❄ Lesson Guide

Objective

By the end of this section, students should be able to clap, tap or stomp a quarter note, eighth note & sixteenth note.

Overview

In this section, students will study different notes, and learn how much musical space each note occupies.

Essential Question

How much musical space do quarter notes, eighth notes and sixteenth notes occupy?

Instruction Tips

Students may have trouble singing "winter wonder" quickly. You can use the playback speed buttons to slow down the video until students have enough practice with the rhythm.

Materials

- Snow Day Video Access
- Workbook pages: 40-50
- Scissors

Table of Contents

Snow Day Song Sheets	40
Rhythm Cards	43
Rhythm Pattern Practice	47
How Many Sixteenth Notes?	48
Quarters, Eighths & Sixteenths	49

Complementary Activities

Make up your own rhythm pattern as a class. Have each student add one of their rhythm cards to the class rhythm to make up a bigger song, then clap, tap or sing the rhythm together.

Section 6.R Video Annotations

0:17 Pause here and ask students which notes they see representing "snowman" and "ice". This is a good time to review quarter and eighth notes.

1:30 Pause here and ask students which notes they see representing "winter wonder. This is a good time to review sixteenth notes.

3:15 Pause here and ask students how many syllables they hear in "ice", "snowman" and "winter wonder".

3:30 Mr. Rob reviews the rhythms practiced in this video.

Snow Day
Lesson 6.R

☆☆☆☆☆

Clap, tap or stomp along while you sing with the sheet music below after you've watched the Snow Day video in section 6.R.

CHORUS 1

It's snow-ing out to-day so, let's go out and play,

Sled-ding and buil-ding snow men.

School's out... HOOR-AY! To-day's our snow day,

Win-ter Won-der ne-ver ends.

VERSE 1

CHORUS 2

It's snow-ing out to-day so, let's go out and play,

Sled-ding and buil-ding snow men.

School's out... HOOR-AY! To-day's our snow day,

Win-ter Won-der ne-ver ends.

VERSE 2

CHORUS 3

It's snow-ing out to-day so, let's go out and play,

Sled-ding and buil-ding snow men.

School's out... HOOR-AY! To-day's our snow day,

Win-ter Won-der ne-ver ends.

VERSE 3

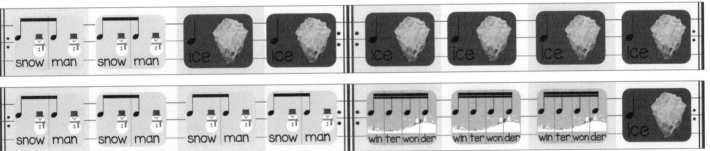

CHORUS 4

It's snow-ing out to-day so, let's go out and play,

Sled-ding and buil-ding snow men.

School's out... HOOR-AY! To-day's our snow day,

Win-ter Won-der ne-ver ends.

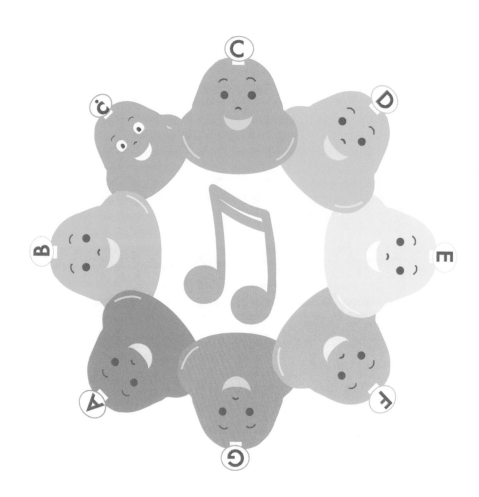

Snow Day Rhythm Cards

Each of the rhythm blocks below fills up one beat.
The faster rhythms have more notes per beat, but all of the blocks
take up the same amount of time.

The Ice has one quarter note.
The Snowman has two eighth notes.
The Winter Wonder has four sixteenth notes.

Cut out each card. Then, lay them out in your own pattern.
When your pattern is ready, try tapping out the pattern on your legs.
Take turns with a partner playing each others rhythms.

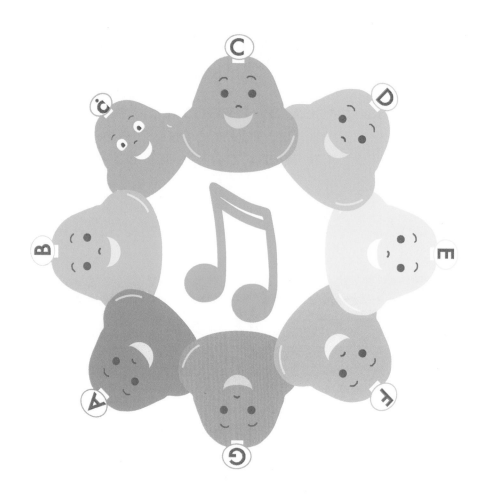

snow | man

snow | man

snow | man

snow | man

win | ter | won | der

win | ter | won | der

win | ter | won | der

win | ter | won | der

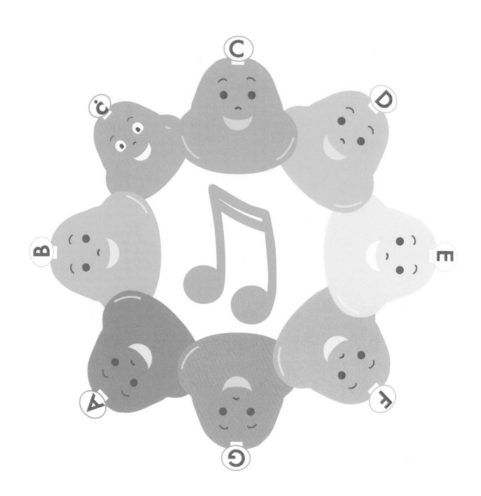

Rhythm Pattern Practice
Complete the patterns below!

   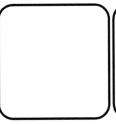  

How Many Sixteenth Notes?

In each row, count the number of sixteenth notes that you see. Hint: count the note heads or stems in the orange boxes! Write down how many you count in each line!

Quarters, Eighths & Sixteenths

Below we have a blank measure and 3 different kinds of notes we can use to fill that measure.

I Measure

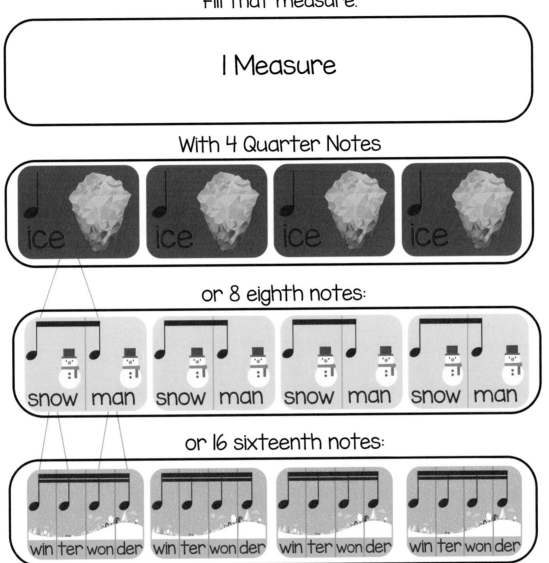

With 4 Quarter Notes

ice | ice | ice | ice

or 8 eighth notes:

snow man | snow man | snow man | snow man

or 16 sixteenth notes:

win ter won der | win ter won der | win ter won der | win ter won der

In the blank spaces below, draw any combination of notes that makes up a complete measure. Use more than one kind of note in each measure.

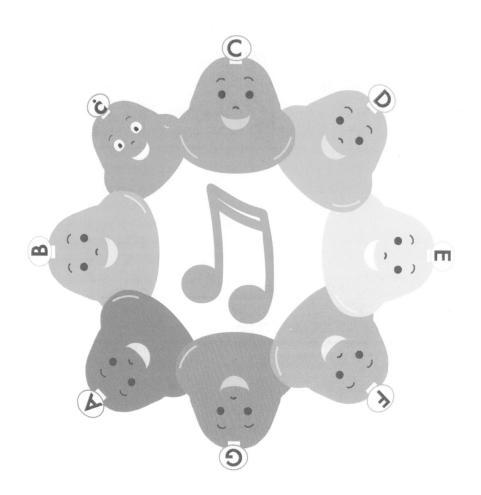

Chapter 6 ♫ Section 4: Dreidel ♫ Lesson Guide

Objective

By the end of this section, students should be able to play "Dreidel".

Overview

In this section, students use the first five notes to play "Dreidel", then review patterning and the colors of notes.

Essential Question

How can a student use the first five notes to play "Dreidel"?

Instruction Tips

As you complete the activities, play the bells, or encourage your student to play the bells. Each time they use a teal, purple or yellow crayon, encourage them to tap that bell as well.

Materials

- C Bell • D Bell • E Bell • F Bell • G Bell
- Red Crayon • Orange Crayon
- Yellow Crayon • Green Crayon • Teal Crayon
- Dreidel Video Access
- Workbook pages: 52-57

Table of Contents

Dreidel Song Sheets	52
Hand-Sign Patterning	54
Write a Song Using G, C & E	55
Color by Note Name	56
Color the Letter	57

Complementary Activities

Ask students to share their original songs with the class. The class could play along in a call and response way with the student-composer leading or help each other write lyrics for one anothers' songs.

Section 6.4 Video Annotations

0:00 Explain to students that in this video they will play another song with just the first five notes: C, D, E, F & G and that they should take out those bells.

1:06 Pause here and remind students that they should be responding to Mr. Rob on their bells, not playing both parts. Call and response is an important part of the learning process.

1:34 Mr. Rob switches from singing colors to the lyrics of "Dreidel".

2:35 Students play and sing along with Mr. Rob instead of using the call and response format.

Dreidel
Lesson 6.4

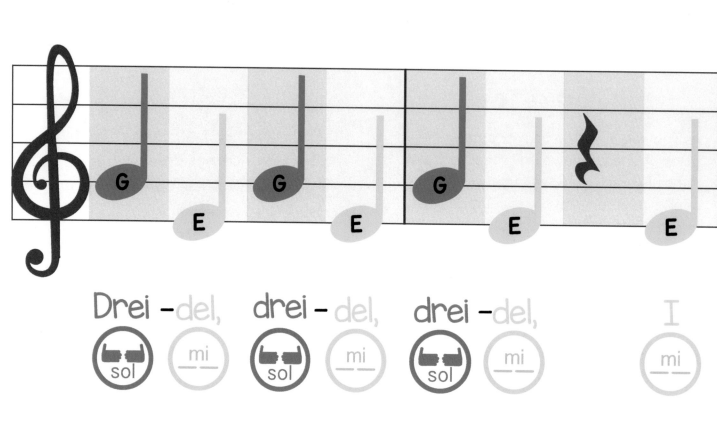

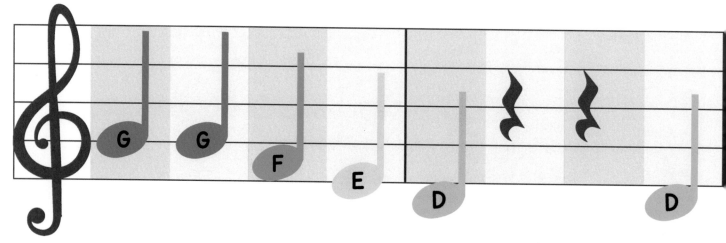

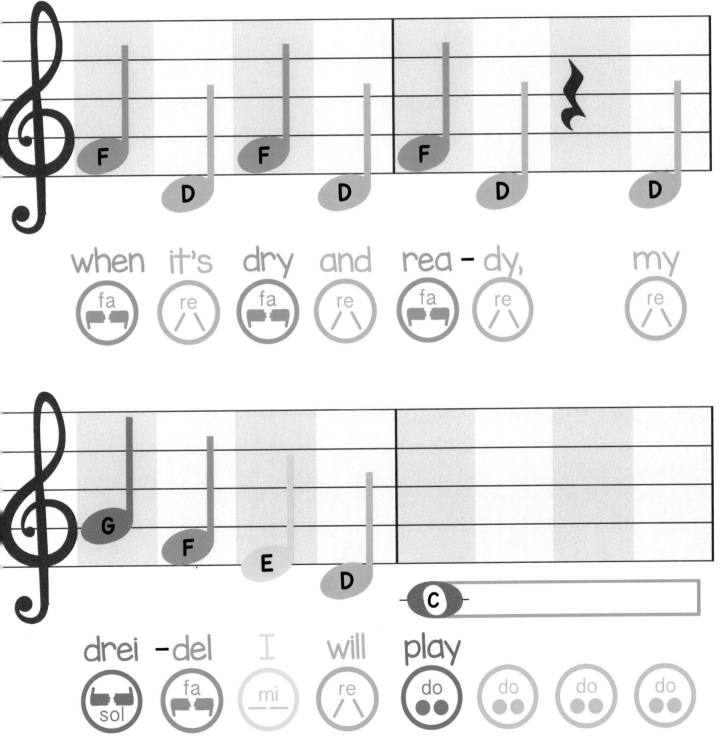

Hand-Sign Patterning

Complete each hand-sign pattern sequence by drawing the correct hand-sign in each empty space. Be sure to sing and hand-sign your complete pattern at the end.

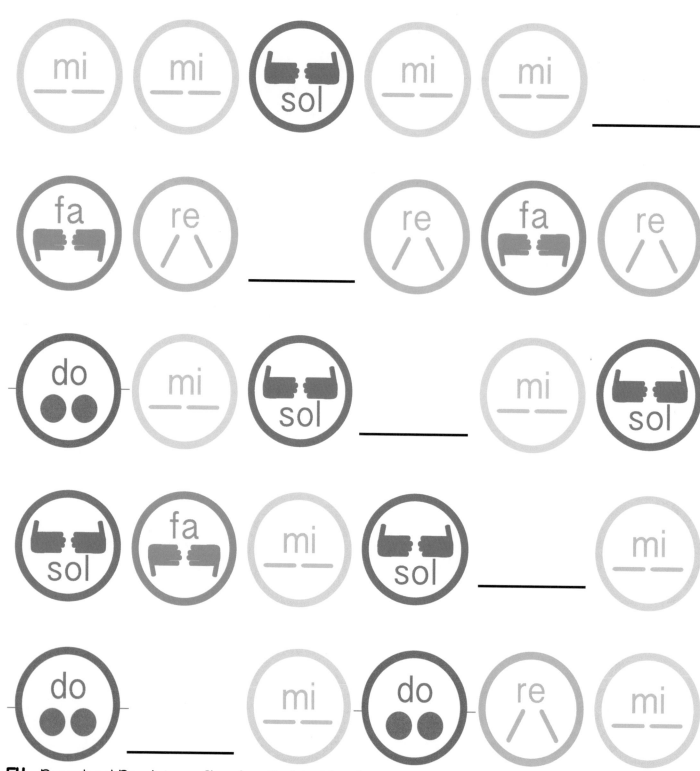

Write a Song Using

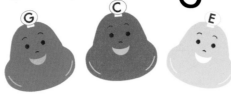

_____ Title   _____ Composer

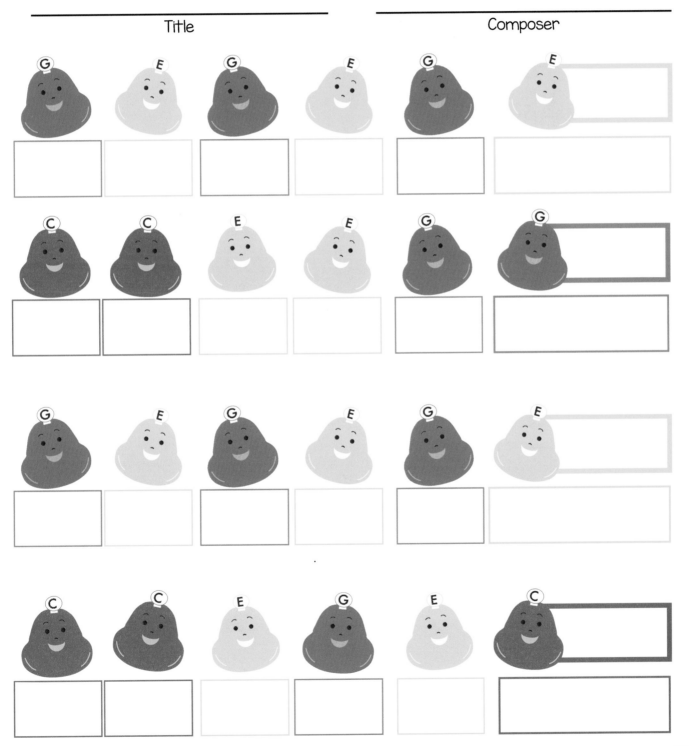

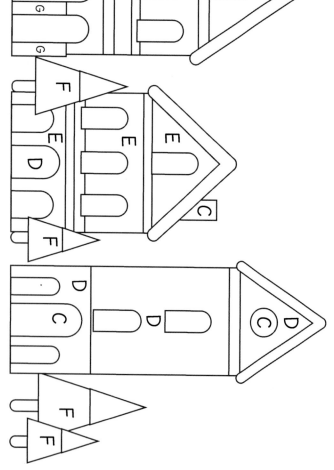

Color by Note Name

Color the Letter
Color the letters to match each bell.

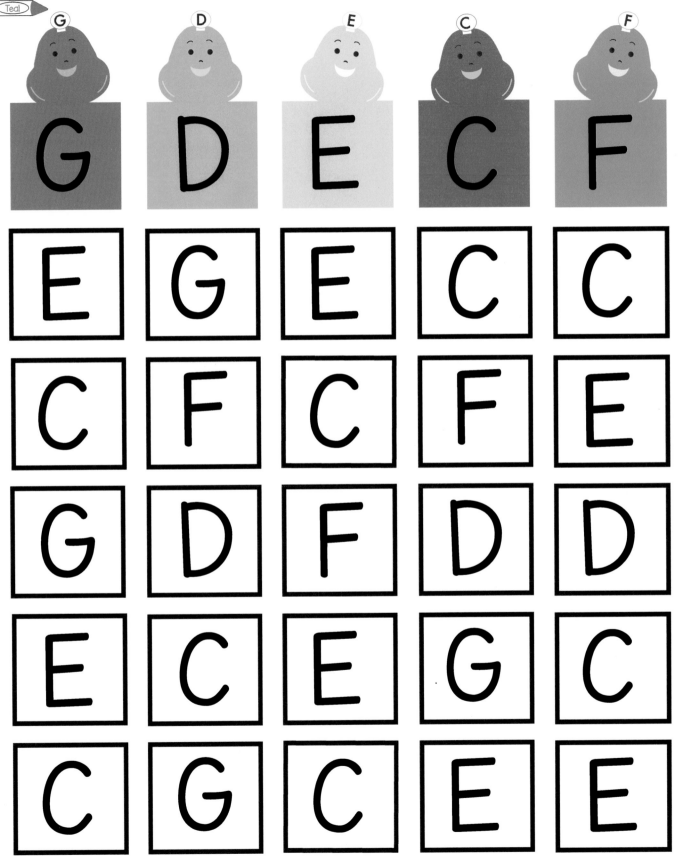

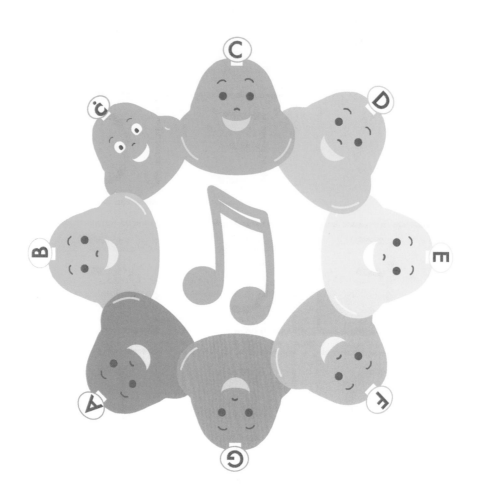

Chapter 6 ❄ Section 5: ...Merry Christmas ❄ Lesson Guide

Objective

By the end of this section, students should be able to play "We Wish you a Merry Christmas".

Overview

In this section, students play "We Wish you a Merry Christmas" first using simple two-note chords, then using individual notes.

Essential Question

How can a student use chords and individiual notes to play "We Wish you a Merry Christmas"?

Instruction Tips

Ask students to compare playing the chords in the video with playing the melody on the song sheets. Which one is easier? Are there any similarities in the notes?

Materials

- C Bell • D Bell • E Bell
- F Bell • G Bell • A Bell
- Red Crayon • Orange Crayon • Yellow Crayon
- Green Crayon • Teal Crayon • Purple Crayon
- We Wish you a Merry Christmas Video Access
- Workbook pages: 60-67

Table of Contents

We Wish you a Merry Christmas

Song Sheets	60
Match the Number	64
Write the Solfège	65
Beat Math	66
Hand-Sign Paths	67

Complementary Activities

Have your learner perform a holiday carol! Ask them to choose someone to perform this song for (even just other students in the class) after they've practiced "We Wish you a Merry Christmas".

Section 6.5 Video Annotations

0:00 Explain to students that in this video they will play a song with the first six notes: C, D, E, F, G & A and that they should take out those bells.

0:17 Pause here to explain to students that they will play this song using simple two note chords, so they should play two bells at one time.

2:04 If students struggled with the pace of this song or playing two bells at one time, go back to 0:17 and play it one more time.

We Wish You A Merry Christmas
Lesson 6.5

☆☆☆☆☆

This song only has 3 beats in each measure... woah!
That means that instead of counting "1 2 3 4" in a measure, we count "1 2 3."

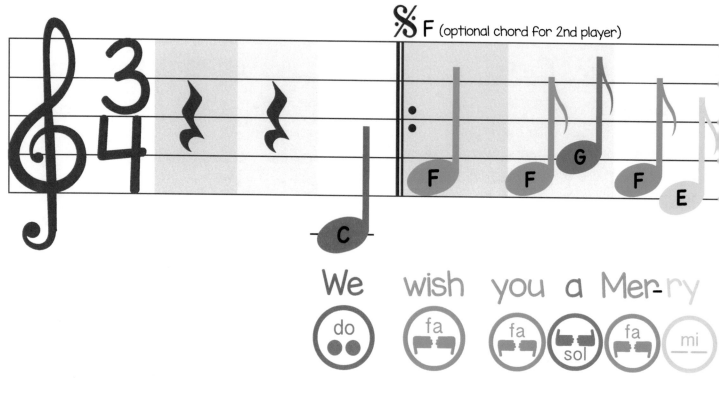

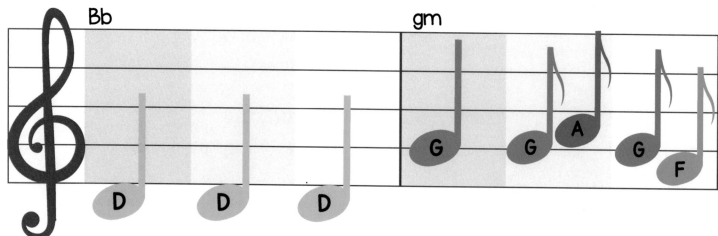

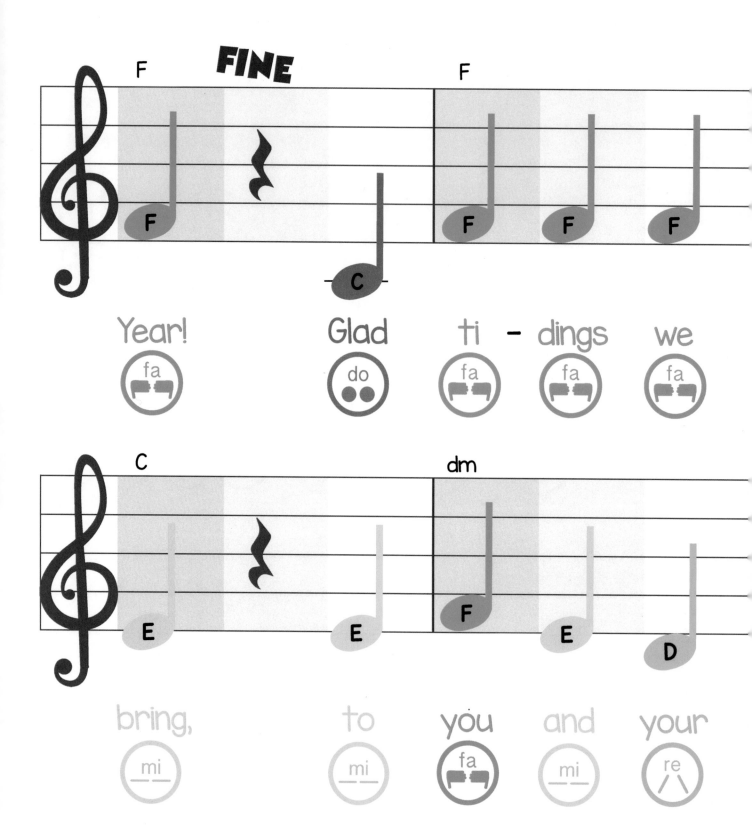

Match the Number

Circle the bell in each box that matches the scale degree.

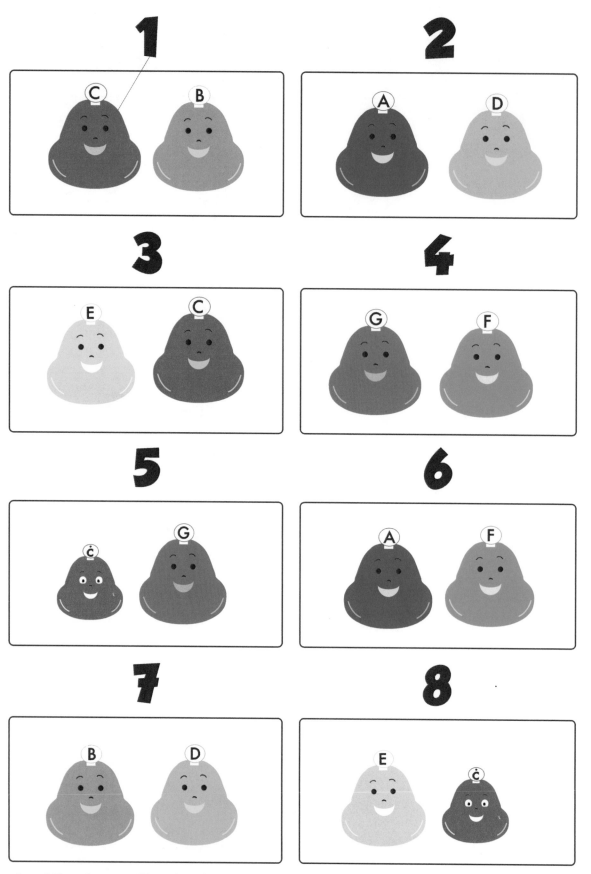

Write the Solfège

In the blank space next to the bells, write the matching Solfège syllable.

Beat Math

This adding activity is a bit harder. To make it easier, write the numbers of beats under each set of notes. You can find the number of beats below.

Hand-Sign Paths

Trace the correct path of the Solfège hand-signs.

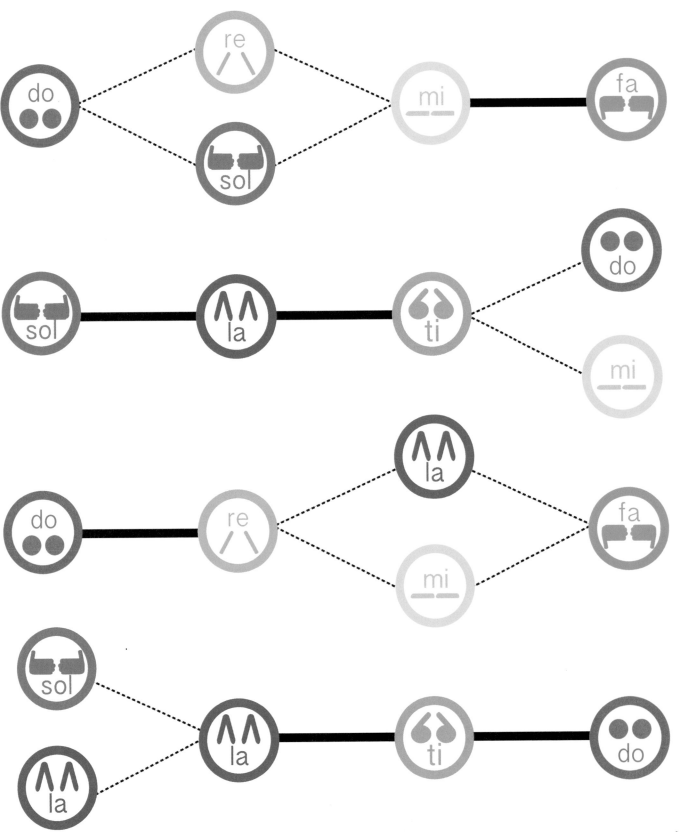

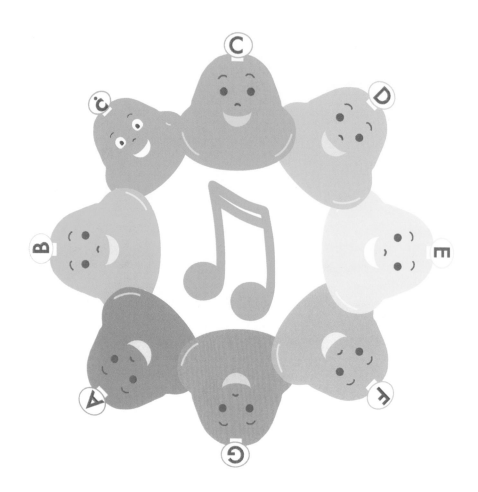

Chapter 6 ♪ Section 6: Auld Lang Syne ♪ Lesson Guide

Objective

By the end of this section, students will be able to play "Auld Lang Syne" using the one chord, the four chord and the five chord.

Overview

In this section, students use the I chord, IV chord and V chord to play "Auld Lang Syne".

Essential Question

How can a student use simplified chords to play "Auld Lang Syne"?

Instruction Tips

Many preschool students have no experience with Roman numerals. If they can't write or identify the Roman numerals right away, it's okay. Keep reinforcing the concept and always refer to the C chord as the one chord; the F chord as the four chord; and the G chord as the five chord.

Materials

- C Bell • D Bell • E Bell
- F Bell • G Bell • A Bell
- Red Crayon • Orange Crayon • Yellow Crayon
- Green Crayon • Teal Crayon • Purple Crayon
- Auld Lang Syne Video Access
- Workbook pages: 70-75

Table of Contents

Auld Lang Syne Song Sheets   70

Chord Matching   72

Roman Numerals Refresher   73

I, IV & V   74

Bell Pattern Practice   75

Complementary Activities

Using these simplified versions of the I Chord, IV Chord and V Chord, play a pattern for your learner to repeat. This will help them practice changing between chords and playing multiple bells at one time.

Section 6.6 Video Annotations

0:00 Explain to students that in this video they will play a song with the first six notes: C, D, E, F, G & A and that they should take out those bells.

0:35 Pause here and review the chords that students will play: a C chord with C & E; a G chord with D & G; and an F chord with F & A. Explain that students will be playing two bells at one time, just like in the last video.

2:14 Mr. Rob reviews the simplified chords used to play "Auld Lang Syne".

Auld Lang Syne
Chord Sheet
Lesson 6.6
☆☆☆☆☆

VERSE 1

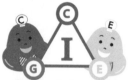 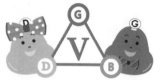

Should auld acquaintance be forgot, and

Never brought to mind.

 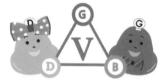

Should auld acquaintance be forgot in,

Days of auld lang   syne.

CHORUS 1

 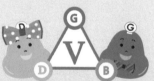  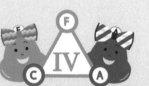

For auld lang   syne my dear,   for auld lang   syne,   we'll

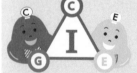 

Take a cup of   kindness yet for

 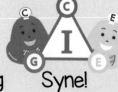

Auld   Lang   Syne!

Using this chord chart, you can play the whole song all by yourself.

1. First, watch the video until you know the song pretty well. Chord charts are good, but you need to know the song a bit first. You should practice playing, singing, and even reading-along with the video.

2. Then, use just this chart and try playing the song without the video! While playing the 2-note chords, sing the words written underneath. Use the words, or lyrics, and your memory of the song to guide you. This is how many musicians learn to read music. Learn it perfectly and perform it on New Year's Eve!

VERSE 2

Now here's a trusting hand my friend, and

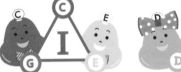

Here's a hand of   mine, we'll

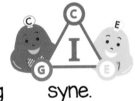

Take a cup of kindness, yet for

   Auld   lang   syne.

CHORUS 2

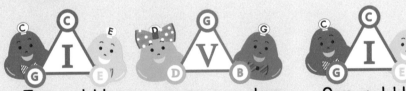

   For auld lang   syne my dear,   for auld lang   syne.

We'll take a cup of kindness, yet for

   Auld   Lang   Syne!

Chord Matching

Each gift box has a chord on top!
If the bells in the box match the chord triangle, color the box.
If the bells do NOT match, draw a big X through the box.

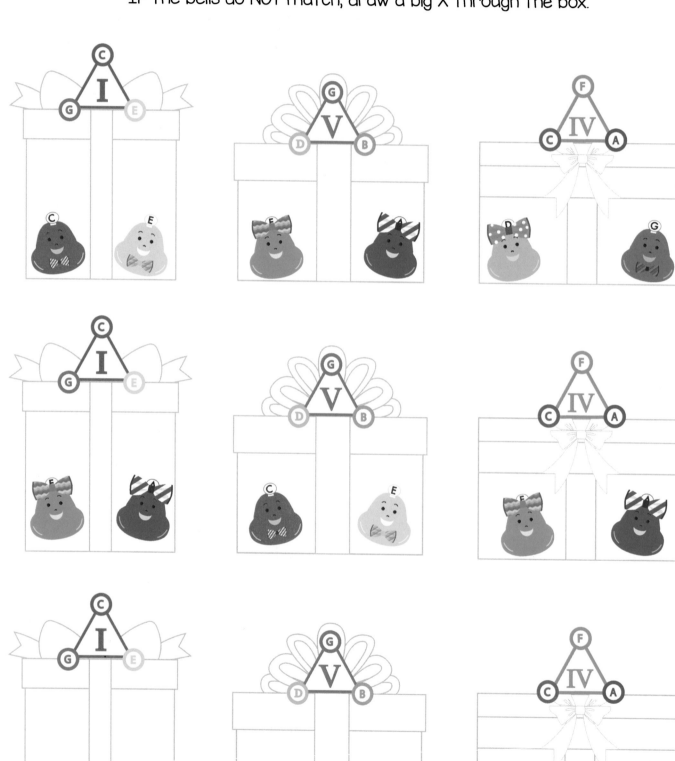

Roman Numerals Refresher

In Roman numerals, I is I and 5 is V.
If you put a I before a V, you get IV, which equals 4.
On the page below, connect the pieces on the right to the I, IV or V.
If it seems tricky, use the colors as a hint!

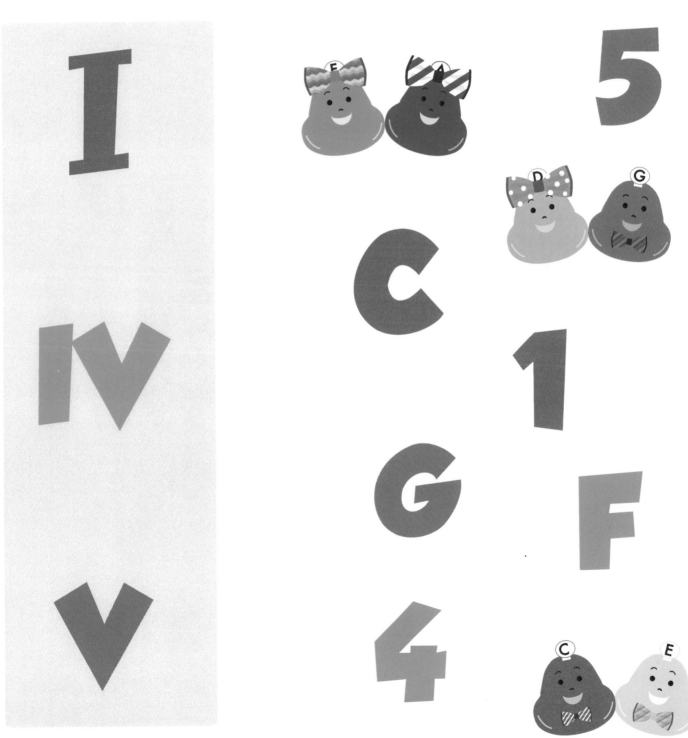

I, IV & V
Circle each Roman numeral that has the correct number of presents under it.

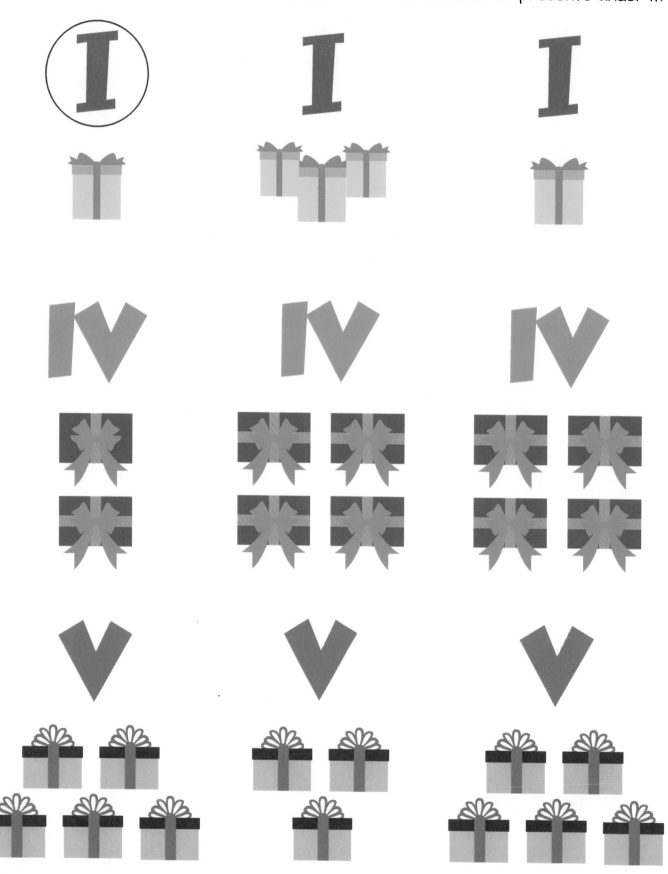

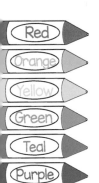

Bell Pattern Practice
Finish the pattern as it appears below.

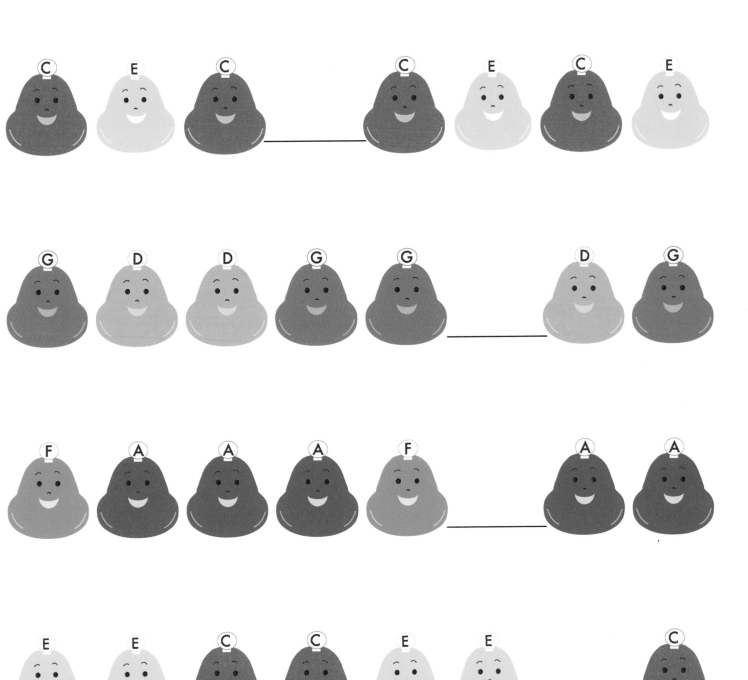

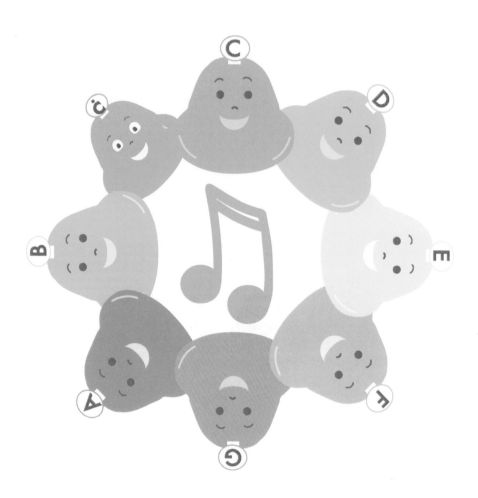

Chapter 6 🎵 Section L: What Note Is It? 🎵 Lesson Guide

Objective

By the end of this section, students should be able to differentiate between F, G and A.

Overview

In this section, students identify the notes F, G and A by ear.

Essential Question

How can a student differentiate between the notes F, G and A?

Instruction Tips

If your students need additional practice, just have them record their answers on a separate piece of paper, or have them hold up the correct hand-sign to indicate their guess.

Materials

- What Note Is It? Video Access
- Workbook pages: 78

Table of Contents

What Note Is It?   78

Complementary Activities

Instead of students guessing along with the video, have them play F, G and A for each other and guess in pairs.

Section 6.L Video Annotations

0:32 Pause and make sure that each student has F, G and A out. Give them time to play each bell and say its note name.

0:46 Pause and let your learner guess the first note name before Rex reveals it!

1:11 Pause and let your learner guess the second note name before Rex reveals it!

1:35 Pause and let your learner guess the third note name before Rex reveals it! Explain to students that this will be the last time you pause before moving on. Be sure that your learner is circling his or her guesses on the What Note Is It workbook page.

What Note Is It?

Use this sheet as you watch. Chapter 6's "What Note Is It?"
Draw a circle around the bell you hear in each box!

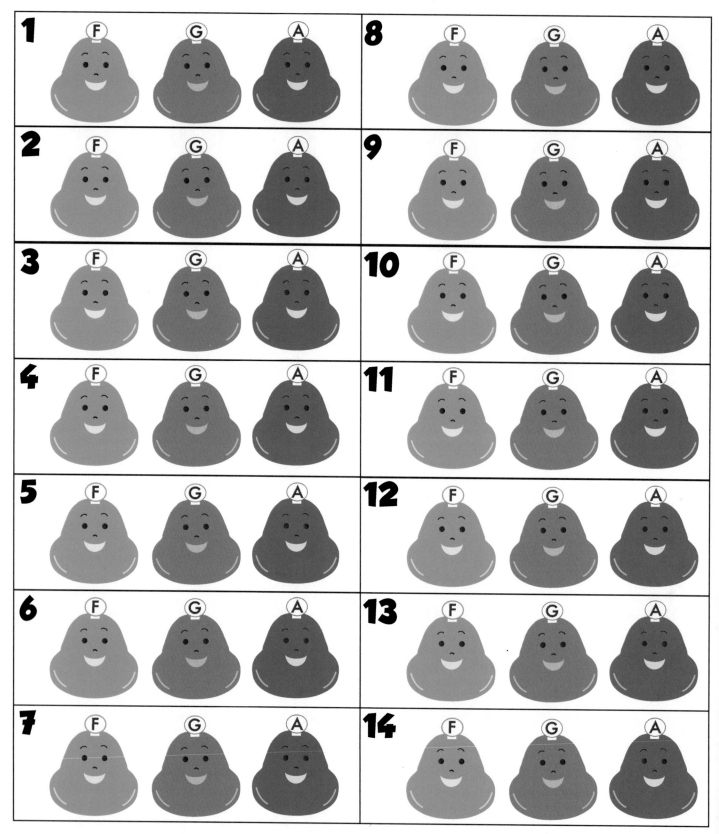

Prodigies Playground

CONGRATULATIONS

You've Completed

Preschool Prodigies

CHAPTER 6

Nice work!

---- Date

---- Teacher Signature

Made in the USA
Columbia, SC
23 January 2019